London Borough of Tower Hamlets

KU-404-622

EVERYBODY WORRIES

EVERYBODY WORRIES

Jon Burgerman

OXFORD
UNIVERSITY PRESS

Even the bravest of the brave

and the coolest of the cool...

...can worry about something big

or worry about something small.

Even the toughest
of the tough

and the smartest of the smart...

...can be worried by noises they hear in the dark.

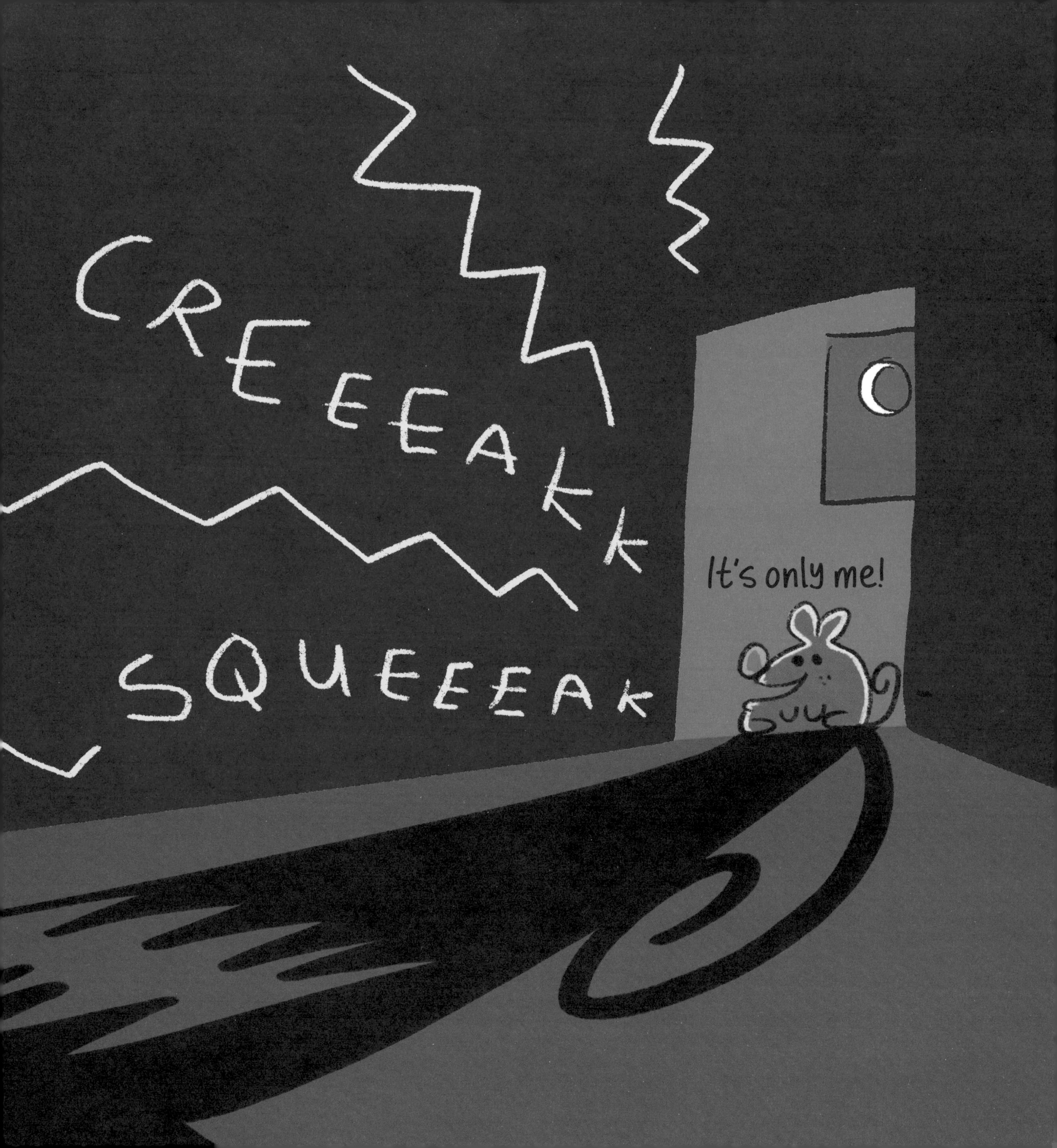
CREEEAKK
SQUEEEAK
It's only me!

What you find worrying

others might find fun.

Worries aren't always the same

for everyone.

Sometimes a big change turns your world upside down

that makes you feel worried and wear a long frown.

Worrying is normal when life's full of change.

It's okay to worry when things don't stay the same.

Your head might ache and your heart beat quickly,
as worries rise like a wave...

...and make you feel sickly.

So when you're worried, talk to a friend—
they might feel the same.

Draw your worries and give them a name.

Take three breaths, slow and deep.

Exercise, eat well, and get enough sleep.

Sharing our worries can help us feel better.

Showing our feelings brings us together.

It's okay to be worried, but it won't last forever.

We can
overcome anything,
when we're there
for each other.

To my brother,
who worries just as much as me.

OXFORD
UNIVERSITY PRESS

Great Clarendon Street, Oxford OX2 6DP

Oxford University Press is a department of the University of Oxford.It furthers the University's objective of excellence in research, scholarship,and education by publishing worldwide. Oxford is a registered trade mark of Oxford University Press in the UK and in certain other countries

Text and Illustrations © Jon Burgerman 2021

The moral rights of the author and illustrator have been asserted
Database right Oxford University Press (maker)

First published 2021

All rights reserved. No part of this publication may be reproduced, stored in a retrieval system, or transmitted, in any form or by any means, without the prior permission in writing of Oxford University Press, or as expressly permitted by law, or under terms agreed with the appropriate reprographics rights organization. Enquiries concerning reproduction outside the scope of the above should be sent to the Rights Department, Oxford University Press, at the address above

You must not circulate this book in any other binding or cover and you must impose this same condition on any acquirer

British Library Cataloguing in Publication Data

Data available

ISBN: 978-0-19-276605-2
Main text set in Burgerman 1.7
with the permission of the author

If your child feels worried or anxious,
here are some agencies that can help:

YOUNG MINDS
A charity offering advice on how to
support your child's mental health.

NHS
Offers advice on managing anxiety in children.

BRITISH PSYCHOLOGICAL SOCIETY
Offers advice on talking to children about illness.

CONTACT
Advice and information for families with disabled children.

THE NATIONAL AUTISTIC SOCIETY
Resources for autistic people and families.

THE SAMARITANS
Free 24-hour support helpline:
Telephone: 116 123

Oxford OWL   Visit **OxfordOwl.co.uk**
for free eBooks and
home learning activities